ENCHANTMENT

A collection of poems, stories and potions

With lots of
love Bella Donna
x
♡

BELLA DONNA
>THE GREEN WITCH<

Charming souls to be free

With illustrations by Abbee Martin

First published in Great Britain in 2021
by Book Brilliance Publishing
265A Fir Tree Road, Epsom, Surrey, KT17 3LF
+44 (0)20 8641 5090
www.bookbrilliancepublishing.com
admin@bookbrilliancepublishing.com

© Copyright Bella Donna 2021
Illustrations by Abbee Martin

A CIP catalogue record for this book is available
at the British Library.

ISBN 978-1-913770-04-4
Typeset in Garamond
Printed by AGM Printers Limited (London, UK)
www.agmprint.co.uk
info@agmprint.co.uk

Words of Love for *Enchantment*

I resonated with many of the poems in this wonderful book, especially *Imagination*, with the lines "It saved me as a child and it awakened me as a woman" and "I realise imagination is short for I- magic-a-nation."

I understand the enchanted world of Fey, and as a Shaman and Healer, I thank this gifted poet for reviving the knowledge of magic and otherworld beings that share this beautiful Blue Planet with us.

Susan Kathleen
#1 Bestselling Author, Journalist
Award-winning Poet & Illustrator

∞

Bella speaks to your soul; she reminds us of who we are on the deepest level and how we reconnect to our inner child. Our medicine is filled with the wisdom Bella shares with simplicity and richness. Bella reminds us of the rawness and magic of nature and the power it holds within us. Keep shining and sharing your sparkle, Bella.

Fiona Clark
The Zenergizer   www.fionaclark.co.uk

Bella, you have used your empathy, love, courage and woman-power to bring us words of strength, support and inspiration. You've not just tapped into your own years of experience but into the very essence of being a strong woman, the magic, and yes, witchcraft, of women, girls, old and young. Thank you for your words, which are both uplifting and grounding, light and deep. Keep writing for us! Love and thanks, Caroline.

Caroline Diehl
www.socialfounder.org
@carolinediehl @socialfounders

∞

Bella Donna's charming collection of poems, meditations and short stories are indeed enchanting. Her words are a fusion of fantasy and reality, filled with warmth, truth, nature, strength and vulnerability. *Enchantment* is engaging story-telling that sings with ancient wisdom and magic. This accomplished debut will fill your heart with joy and compassion and will allow to feel connected with the natural world - perfect for these strange times in which we live.

Olivia Eisinger
Editor

Dedicated to:
My beloved, Andrew.
My greatest creations: Ben, Adam, Abbee
and William.
My Guru, Forest the Labrador

Special acknowledgements to my amazing daughter,
the illustrator of this book.
The young and talented Goddess
at the beginning of a magical journey.

Contents

Foreword

The poems and stories in this enchanting collection come from a deeply personal place, so it is only fitting that this Foreword is personal too. I have suffered with anxiety all my life. I think that often we are anxious because we believe the world is more complicated than it is. The pieces in this book are the perfect antidote to this, stemming as they do from a place of stillness and simplicity: "how simple life is". Notice that I said 'simple', and not 'simplistic'. The latter implies a lack of depth, whilst the former encompasses the fullness of the universe. It allows us to swim with mermaids and talk to the girl in the oak tree.

Anxiety also involves trying to have more control. The ethereal pieces in this book are all about letting go, relinquishing that yearning for control, and coming to terms with what the universe has in store for us. They implore us to sit still, quietly yielding to the fact that "there is a deep knowing that everything just is". This does not imply simple capitulation to the whims and vagaries of circumstance; we each need to sit at the 'Head of the Table', maintaining a place of stillness amongst the chaos. Some things we can control, and others we can't: "the party is mine, the table is mine", even though the guests might sometimes enter uninvited. It is up to all of us to take tea with whomever we choose.

It is important that the universe offers up a range of shadows; it is not all flowers and meadows, for life finds its worth against this shadowy backdrop. As the poet adumbrates, "only someone who has laid in thistle can rest in a buttercup". Once we acknowledge that what seems like Death is really just Fear, and thus call it by its proper name, this looming entity shifts from a terrifying demon to a mere field mouse, and we are "no longer caged" by the prisons we have built around ourselves. We can befriend the Elephant of Grief and grow trees with the Hat of Fear. Even if Sadness doesn't want to play, we can hug her anyway. Don't be afraid of peeking through the door.

And I breathe...

Joshua Seigal
www.joshuaseigal.co.uk | @joshuaseigal
Author and poet
Winner of 2020 Laugh Out Loud Award

Introduction

The idea for *Enchantment* was born out of love. As a nurse, at the beginning of the Covid-19 pandemic I was sent out into the community to support terminal patients. I noticed in between patients that the streets were empty. I pulled my car over and began to weep. As I looked up, I saw a painting of a rainbow in someone's garden. Instantly within, I heard my inner child say, "It's okay." I became overwhelmed yet realised that my inner child had so much to offer.

I have been writing poetry for many years. It was not until that moment I understood these poems came from my inner child. A switch was turned on. Finally, I could release the feelings associated with others judging me as being childish, immature and unintelligent.

I knew that the power within me was thanks to the connection with my inner child, who is wise, playful and powerful.

The words of my poems in this book came to me always when I was in nature and sometimes in my dreams. I found these situations to be healing and infusing me with an energy that enabled me to be who I was born to be and free.

During this whole enlightened episode, I found the courage and felt strong enough to embrace 'Bella the Green Witch', who was always a part of me.

Poetry is a medium to be read aloud. The little girl within me loves to sing. I dare you to read these enchanted poems, stories and other magic potions aloud and open up your heart to feel the inner child magic within.

Love

The Green Witch

INSPIRATIONS

The following poems and writing were whispered to me on the wind. Just as I have been inspired, I trust they will inspire you too.

Rain

And she rains... right on cue
Every drop a bringer of life.
Sacred water.
Sacred land.
Drink.
So much beauty
Gratitude.

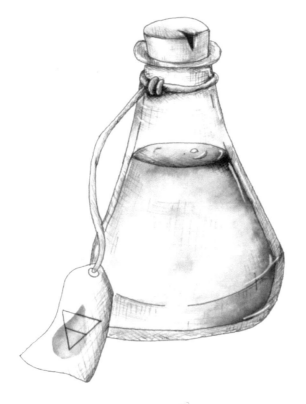

Father Sky

All I know is that when I look at you
Whatever my question was, my doubts, my fears,
my anger...

When I look up at you, as my shoulders drop
And my chest opens,
All my questions fall to the earth
And I forget what the questions were.
I even forget what the word 'question' means
And there is a deep knowing that everything just is.

The Girl, the Oak Tree and Me

There's a girl who sits in the tree.
I sit on the log on the earth
and I talk to the tree.
She sits and listens,
joyfully swinging her legs.
Inviting me to play.

Sometimes I do
and we'll strip off
and run through the woods,
or we'll splash in puddles,
or dig in the dirt.

Sometimes I don't.
She's ok with that,
she's just happy that
I notice her now.
So she'll sit, swinging her legs
and when I'm sad,
she'll climb down and sit next to me.

She doesn't understand,
she's just a child.
But she just sits next to me.
There's so much power
in that.

So I'll sit with her
and I sit with my tree,
a beautiful, wise Oak,
strong, covered in scars,
who communicates with me
without words, and
teaches me to feel with my ears
and listen with my heart.

Who openly shows me
the beauty of trusting
in the cycle of all things.

Our roots now deeply entwined.
We sit; the girl,
the Oak Tree and me.

Between the three of us, we get by.

Enchantment

How Simple Life Is

How simple life is
As time uncoils, dissipates - becomes translucent.
As you lift the veil,
peer through the hollow bone
And behold the golden pool of existence
as it ripples and reflects back at you.
Your own luminosity.

How simple life is
beneath the layers.
The shadow that is made of dust.
The candle that burns so brightly
Gently flickering as you breathe.
The essence, tastes, colours, shapes
That you relish, all here.
The universe in one drop.

Enchantment

How simple life is
As you float softly expanding
and contracting with it all.
At home, cupped
in the hands of your heart.

At home in the arms of the mother.
Simple, gentle, emptiness oferflówan.

Last Night

Last night in my unsettled sleep
What crazy dreams!
A night when I know I've been sleepwalking.
I am visited by a dark, hooded figure.

She lays down next to me on the bed
Her long, gnarly, bony fingers reach out to me.
She wraps them tightly around my wrist.
"I am death," she says in a low tormenting voice.

I gaze deeply into her eyes
Pools of empty darkness.
"I know you," I say.
"You are not death, you are fear."

Her face softens. Her grip loosens.
A warm gentle flame flickers in the back of her
eyes.
"Thank you for seeing me," she says.
"I just came to hold your hand."

Enchantment

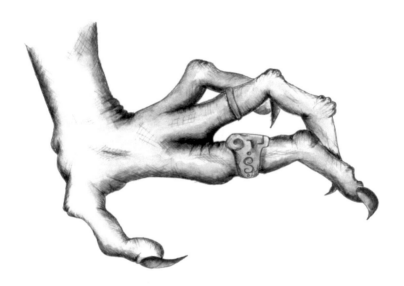

Pyracantha

As I lay in my hammock,
Underneath the blossoming Pyracantha
And the big, wide, blue sky,
I rest in the warmth; in my shift.
Rocking gently.
Feeling held.

The bees are busy
bathing themselves in her blooms.
And the fairies swing and play
in her branches of thorns,
gently blowing her sweet, sensual smell,
becalming me.

I wonder, as I float here
my body feeling tired and heavy,
Why Pyracantha is so unloved?
Yes, she has thorns
But she uses these
to protect herself.

She welcomes all
inviting her fruit to spread her message of love.
How beautiful is that?
I give praise to Pyracantha, friend of Hawthorn.
And I give thanks to all of nature,
my medicine, my love.

Water Nymph

As I sit on the river bank,
She invites me to explore.
Here I lay, warm, in the sun,
Content in my denial
And her head pops up out of the water.

I notice the pull to climb in.
I also notice the voice inviting me to stay,
Where I am warm and safe.
But the Water Nymph's
call is stronger.

I dip my toes into the water,
she waits patiently for me.
It feels cool, uninviting.
Mesmerised,
the ripples and the flow speak to me.

As I step deeper into the water
It's fingleice freezing.
My nice warm flesh feels
like it's being stung,
It doesn't feel delicious at all.

The river bank calls me back to safety, warmth,
Relaying stories of what might happen if I stay.
If I stay with her,
moving with the motion
E-Motion.

As I drop right in - I succumb!
She holds my hand
And I dive right under.
My skin tingles and burns
My head is on fire
I hold on tightly to my breath.

Until I have to breathe, to let go.
So much pressure, so suffocating
Yet I breathe and it hurts
I breathe in the water deep.
She holds my hand.

We are moving.
Moving with the current
Flowing down river
To the ocean.
I feel the current pulling, pushing, guiding me.

When we reach the ocean
My head bobs to the top
The waves crash over me.
She pulls me down, I feel it, I feel it all
Every cell in my body feels.

We drop down, deep down.
The waves now thundering above me
As we drop. Drop.
There's a pause
I am floating…

She holds my hand.
I let go, surrender, accept.
There is no joy, no pain.
A stillness
A silence like no other.

She lets go of my hand.
I stop kicking my legs.
Stop paddling my hands.
I let go.
My hair billowing around me.
I am here
Deep within

Being held
Still
Floating
Emptiness
Nothing
Nothing
Nothing, yet everything.

All is effortless
All is graceful grace.
All just is.
There are no words.
I am the ocean.
I listen to the call.

What If...

What if
you looked over the edge
and the tightness in your chest, the palpitations,
the cold sweats, the shakes, the fast breathing,
the sheer panic as your mind screams
NO, were all there... and you jumped anyway.

What if
you put your trust into the unknown
and let things unfold as they will.
What if, in reality, we actually have no control
over anything,
and everything is playing out as it should.

What if,
in this place of surrender and letting go,
you stumble across your own magnificence,
beaming back at you. And it's the presence,
the essence of YOU, creating the
tightness in your chest, palpitations, cold sweats,
the shakes, fast breathing, and your body is
screaming... YES.

What if
we spend our lives climbing glass mountains.
What if...

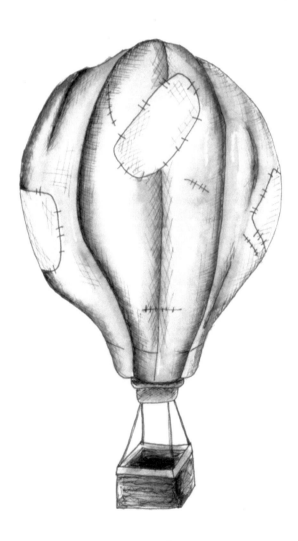

Between Worlds

Do you see the unseen,
Can you feel the spaces between it all?
Can you see with your ears
And hear with your eyes?

Is the magic that unfolds for you,
In that pause between each breath?
Can you float and expand here
In this space
In this place,
In between worlds?

Explore the magical world within you
And the gifts that you bring back
To here and now, this world,
Will be without end.

She

She is no longer caged.
She who used to sit, curled up,
starving, emaciated, angry.
No longer locked up,
No longer ignored.
She speaks to me and I to her.
She, the dark Witch within me.
My strength, my power, my shadow and light.

Sometimes she will show up
With a swear word or cuss.
She will surprise me as her words leave my mouth.
But how good it feels to release
the word Frugglepuff.

Other times she will visit
when I feel sad.
A deep ache in my heart will call her.
I sit in her earthy presence
She grounds and comforts me.

Enchantment

And there are those days when
I am busy or distracted.
She will whisper to me on the breeze.
Or glisten in a raindrop on a leaf,
To catch my eye.

The days when I completely ignore her,
She will call to me with bird song,
In the running water of my kitchen tap,
And in the corners of my bedroom,
In the shadows... and she will scream.

She can no longer tolerate
not being heard.
She accepts just an acknowledgement,
that I love her
but I'm not up for interacting right now.

And, of course, there are days,
When I can completely embody her.
Her flames consume me.
I feel her power, her strength.
My heartbeat rapid.

And she guides me past my edges,
My boundaries, my patterns.
She lifts the cage that surrounds me
And gives me more space
to explore with curiosity.

Then I retreat for a time,
Like a child moving away from a hot fire,
To safety and rest.
She understands that I cannot
stand in her flames all the time.

And she is content, as am I,
that whilst we used to be strangers,
We have become acquaintances, good friends.
And one day when the moon sits right,
We will be lovers.

Enchantment

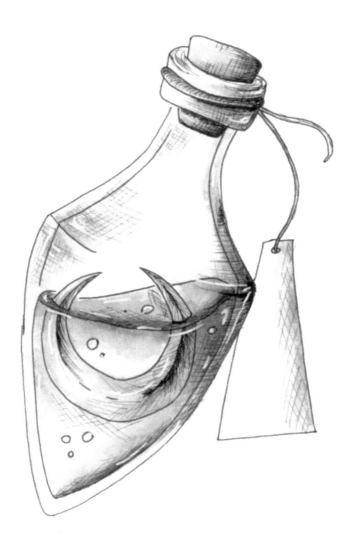

Mermaid Tears

As I lay in the dark, rich, gloopy mud
Face down, tears, they flow.
They flow and flow.
Until I am laying in a pool of my own sorrow.

And still more come.
There's a soothing female voice,
urging me to stay a while.
The tears come like waves flooding over me.

Until I have cried myself an ocean.
I am the ocean. The voice is the ocean.
So I lay face down in the mud
In the depths of the ocean, made of my tears.

As I look down at where my feet would be
I give my tail a flick.
Around me there is stillness, darkness, peace
Serenity, safety, holding.

Enchantment

The creatures of the deep approach me.
I know them well, I know this place well.
Deep in the darkest depths of me...
I feel held.

I sit up, my hair billowing around me
My being, naked and open
The light from the distant moon. She
Gently kisses my breasts.

I am light, movement here is effortless.
The creatures of the deep gather around
And we sit in a circle.
There is no talking.
Only the power of our magic.
Words are not necessary.

They are grateful.
My tears have restored them
They now have so much space to move around.
I leave them to gently swim in solitude.

Exploring the depths of my ocean
I feel graceful, feminine, strong,
Nurtured by
Mermaid tears.

I don't know how long I stayed
Swimming, dancing, crying.
I fell asleep, in touch with my own depths,
my femininity, my grace, my love, my ocean,
my power...

and I slept well.

Enchantment

Curl Up Buttercup

Today when I got home from work,
all I wanted to do was curl up.
Listening to that call, I lay
on my side in a foetal position.
And gently closed my eyes.

I tuned into my breath,
Inhale, exhale; inhale, exhale; inhale, exhale
in and out each time, allowing my bones
to drop deeper into Mother Earth.
Offering them to She.

I arrived in a lush green meadow,
full of buttercups.
As I walked through the meadow,
I began to shrink.
Each step, smaller and smaller - a field mouse.

Climbed into a buttercup. I curled up
and lay on the velvety, yellow bed.
Cupped, held. Warm, safe.
Gently swaying on the breeze. I rocked
until I felt ready to climb out and return...

The Head of My Table

Every day when I sit at the Head of my Table
there's a likeness to the Mad Hatter's Tea Party!

I carefully lay all the place mats and cutlery.
I place flowers in the centre,
lay out the cups and saucers, teapots.
All before I have drawn breath.
I take my place at the Head of my Table
waiting for my guests…

Everyday there is a new guest
but more often there are the regular visitors.
The first to be seated are Anger and Fear.
I'm sure to dish them up an equal size of Love Pie,
oftentimes they can be so quarrelsome.

Next, we have Joy and Sorrow,
who come hand in hand.
I nod, they sit
and I tend to them.

Quietly, oh, so quietly enter Sadness and Shame.
They steal so softly sometimes I do not notice
them and they spend some time in silence without
any pie.
When I do notice, I am sure to offer them a large
slice of Love Pie and a cup of Acceptance Tea.

And then of course enters Ego.
He always tries to take my seat.
He loves to be Head of the Table.
But with Pie and Tea I can entice him
quite nicely,
with a squirt of cream and a cherry...
He's quite fickle that way.

Last but not least are Peace and Happiness.
More often than not they sit together
and they are happy to share the same Pie.

'Good Gracious,' you may say, 'what a busy party!'
Well, some days I hide under the table
and eat the Pie myself.
But more often they will kick me,
sometimes with their boots.

So I sit back at the Head of my Table
and in the loudness when Laughter visits,
I seat her and we giggle
at the silliness of it all.

And on some days... some... it is quieter and only a
few come to tea.
Either way, the party is mine, the Table is mine,
the pots and all, and I take Tea with
whomever I choose.

Imagination

My imagination, my precious gift, my gateway,
I am so grateful.

It saved me as a child and it
awakened me as a woman.

The more I connect with
my imagination, the more I get to know myself.

From this deep pool of self-knowledge,
I become curiouser and curiouser.

I meet more people like me and realise
imagination is short for

I- magic-a-nation.

Let Nature Find You

May the sound of the birds open your ears.
May the sights of spring beauty, in the forests,
meadows and gardens around you, open your eyes.
May the smell of the rain and freshly cut grass,
tune you into your breath, as you breathe in earth's
delectable nectar.
May a beautiful spring flower, cupped gently in the
palm of your hand, remind you, that you can feel.
May the scent of the ocean and the awakening
earth, softly land on your palette, reminding you of
the taste of home.
And as you journey across your own landscape,
your feet deeply rooted in the earth...
May you notice, as the sun shines on your face, that
your shadow stands alongside you, playfully inviting
you to dance and explore. All of you.

The beauty. The shadow. The flame. The All.

Let nature find you
As you find your nature.
Your you.

My Belly

With my hand upon my belly
I can feel a softness here.
Unlike before, I enjoy this softness
I have found in my body.
Before, my body had to be hard, strong, tall,
and ready for battle.
Now she is soft, loving, gentle, open.

... open, oh yes, open.
But open you say, is that not vulnerable?
Oh yes it is and here I am, here in my vulnerability.
Showing this part of myself to the world.
This place is not weak, it's a place where you can
feel and love.
It is home.
My soft place, my belly.

For all my beautiful sisters out there,
put one hand on your belly,
one hand on your heart and breathe.

You are beautiful, you are loved.
If I could hug you right now,
I would squeeze you so hard
if that would make you feel beautiful.

It won't, this journey is yours.
But know you are not alone.

Beauty in the Shadows

Some days I wake and the weight of the
world lays heavy on me.
It sits on my chest and restricts my breath,
It fills my eyes with lakes and my chest with
fire and pain.
I try to hate the world and all it has to offer me.

But then I hear the birds sing their melody,
I hear them singing the truth of what is.
I hear the breeze through my window
whisper, 'You have breath.'

I feel the gentle embrace of my warm bed
covers on my skin,
and the softness of my pillow holding
my heavy head.

I smell the scents of Autumn outside and
I picture their beauty, their colours,
the abundant wildlife busy beginning a new day.
And... as much as my mind is telling me
to hate this world, I cannot.

There is far too much beauty, beauty that
sits on my chest and restricts my breath.
There is Beauty that fills my eyes with lakes
and my heart with fire and pain.
Beauty that calls me to listen, to feel, to touch,
to love, to evolve, to awaken.
And all is as it is.

Thank You Grief

Thank you sun for shining on my grief
Warming my body, my flesh, my heart,
Thank you breeze for blowing on my face
Cooling me, reminding me I too have breath.

Thank you rain and clouds
For enveloping me in my sadness and
gently rocking me there.

Thank you Mother Earth for holding me
Always, always, always.

Thank you grief for showing me the depths
of my love for my daddy…

Only Someone

Only someone who has been
Deeply touched by sadness
Can truly feel the joy.

Only someone who has felt
a thousand stings
Can feel a thousand tingles.

Only someone who has
Put themselves last
Can begin to put themselves first.

Only someone
Who has laid in thistle
Can rest in a buttercup.

Only someone who has walked
Barefoot across stones
Can truly feel the soft green grass
Kissing their feet.

Only someone who has
Sat through the darkest night
Can feel the sunrise in the morning.

Only those who believe there is more,
More in the silence
More in the dark corners
Will find it…

Only someone.

POEMS

Everyone loves a rhyme.
With pen in hand it's now the time
To mark on paper from the start,
Poems revealed from my heart.

My Book

With my pen in my hand
And my heart on a hook,
I weave all my magic
Into a book.

I weave in the trees
And all of the flowers.
A bright summer's day
And some April time showers.

I weave in a spider
A beautiful sky.
The scent of a rose
And a bird flying by.

A sprinkle of moon dust
Some Fae in a tree.
A sleeping green dragon
And a large pot of tea.

A snail on a journey
A witch and her hat.
A storm in a teacup
And an Oak tree chat.

I weave in a mermaid
A rose cauldron stew
But most of all…
I weave in YOU!

The Fairy in the Woods

There's a fairy in the woods my friend,
Why don't you come and see?
There's a fairy in the woods my friend,
While you sit there, drinking tea.

There's a fairy in the woods my friend,
She has so much to say.
She talks of love, of laughter, joy
Why don't you come and play?

The fairy in the woods my friend,
Is getting rather bored.
She wants us both to play with her
She will not be ignored.

You sit there, fine, I do not mind
I'm going to go and play
And the fairy in the woods and I
Will have a lovely day.

And we did, that fairy in the woods and I,
We played late into the eve
Next time, when she calls again
Maybe you will believe?

The Witch Who Buried Her Hat

Don't bury your hat, the voice it said.
Don't bury your hat my dear.
But ignore it she did, she buried her hat.
She buried it out of fear.

And there it sat beneath the earth,
Fermenting hour by hour.
Until one day it grew into
A magical Hawthorn flower.

The fairies swung from the boughs of the Bush,
Such a wondrous sight to behold.
They realised how this Bush had grown,
They knew she had to be told.

That eve, the fairies sent her a message,
A message upon the breeze.
To come to the forest, to come and see
The magical Hawthorn trees.

The girl arrived half-awake, half-asleep.
And the beauty was much to behold.
She dropped herself down and how she did weep.
Unaware, she hadn't been told.

The fairies spoke and they did say
"This magical tree that grew,
We had to tell you, you had to know,
Because it belongs to you."

"It's yours to keep my love," they said
"It's yours to keep my dear,
As much as we love to play in its boughs,
It whispers your name, can't you hear?"

And sure enough, she heard the voice,
The long-lost voice of home.
She fell to the earth and began to dig
Like a dog with the scent of a bone.

The hat it appeared beneath the soil,
She donned it upon her head.
Her magic returned, her body alive
All a-tingle with sparkles, she said,

"Oh, you're my love and I solemnly swear,
That I'll never give you away!"
The fairies they smiled
As she danced through the woods,
With a Hop and a Whoop and a Yaaay!

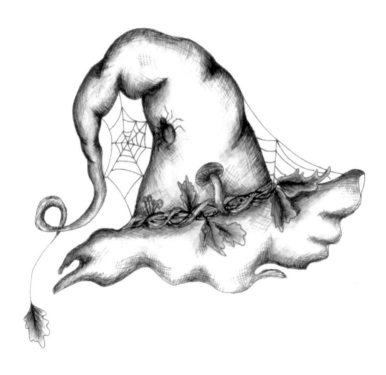

The Fairy in the Rose

There's a fairy in her petals
as pretty as can be.
Asleep amongst her plumage
So magical to see.

She makes a gentle humming noise
As she rests there fast asleep.
The scent of the rose has enchanted her
So gingerly I peep.

She wears a pretty pink dress
That matches her pearly pink lips.
Her hair so soft and delicate
Oh, how my heart it skips.

I know I mustn't touch her
I would not interrupt.
I watch her in her beauty
My softly filling cup.

The Elephant in the Room

There's an elephant in the room my friends,
The elephant's name is Grief.
He sits there in the corner.
The elephant is a thief.
He steals away my happiness
My peacefulness and joy.
The elephant in the room my friends,
he sits there to annoy.

There's an elephant in the room my friends,
He likes to take up space
And every time I smile or laugh
He's right there in my face.
The elephant in the room my friends,
Likes watching me in pain.
He reminds me of this missing void
Again and again and again.

There's an elephant in the room my friends,
It's getting really tough.
He follows me everywhere I go
I've really had enough.
He follows me to bed at night
When I just need to sleep and rest.
He climbs up on the covers
And he sits there on my chest.

There's an elephant in the room my friends,
He made me scream and shout
"Just get out of my space you freak,
I don't want you about!"
"But here I am regardless
And here I'll stay," he said.
I didn't realise that Grief could talk
As I toddled off to bed.

There's an elephant in the room my friends,
He let me sleep that night.
In the early morning sunrise
I simply gave up the fight.
I let go of holding on
I let emotions flow
I let everything come
And finally let everything go.

There's an elephant in the room my friends,
The elephant's name is Grief.
This elephant is a friend of mine,
I like to call him Keith.
He sits there and he listens to me
Speaking only when he must
The elephant is a friend of mine
An elephant I can trust.

Mr Cricket

In the shade of the Ash tree
Where the long grass grows,
I met Mr Cricket
he tickled my toes.

I'm sitting connecting
with this big old tree.
Mr Cricket comes up
and interrupts me.

He's wearing a hat,
The bowler hat kind.
"I wanted to talk to you.
I hope you don't mind?"

"Of course not," I replied
Surprised he could talk.
"Come sit on my shoulder,
We'll go for a walk."

Enchantment

He hopped upon my shoulder
Lighter than air.
We walked through the forest
A beautiful pair.

We chatted for hours
The Cricket and I.
Of things on our minds
and the time flew by.

As the sun was setting
And he had to go.
I kissed him with gratitude
He said "Cheerio!"

In the shade of the Ash tree
Where the long grass grows.
I met Mr Cricket,
he tickled my toes.

Zing

I seem to have lost my Zing my love,
I seem to have lost my Zing.
I'd borrow it from someone else my love,
But that's just not the thing.

My Zing she is so beautiful
Have you seen her anywhere?
She's not there in the wardrobe
She's not even under the chair.

She's not there in the music,
She's not there in my song,
She's not there in my dancing,
There must be something wrong.

Do you think she's up and left me?
Do you think she's gone for good?
I'm searching for her everywhere
She's not even in the wood.

Enchantment

She's not there in my drum sound
Or shining in the sun.
She's not there in the meadow.
Where is it she has run?

I glance down into my teacup
In the deepest of despair
Why has she gone and left me?
Does she no longer care?

My tears begin to flow
And as they trickle down my face
I accept the possibility
That she has left this place.

She's gone to help another
My precious little Zing,
And in this moment of acceptance
I see her in everything.

She shows up in my teardrops
A warm tingling that I know,
And soon I begin to realise
She actually didn't go.

She was there all the time
Hiding when I was seeking.
In my neediness to find her
I couldn't hear her speaking.

For she is made of feeling,
And feelings you can't feel
When you're seeking and you're grasping,
You leave no room to heal.

So, the moment when you surrender
You trust and you let go
Your Zing will walk beside you
Sowing seeds for you to grow.

Curl up

Curl up
Drop down
Give in
Let go
Tell her the things
You want her to know.

Make sounds
Move through
Pick up
Let be
Give them to she.
She'll build us a tree.

The Magick

What we seek is already here.
Day after day, year after year.
It never leaves us, we're already home.
It's just underneath distrust and unknown.

But it speaks to us quietly, loud enough to hear.
In the song of the blackbird or the taste of a tear.
It speaks of enchantment of magick and love.
Within and without, below and above.

In all the small things, the magick resides,
In the beautiful moon and her moving tides.
In the smell of cut grass and the rustling of leaves.
In the tiniest of spiders and the webs that she
weaves.

In the smile of a stranger and the touch of soft skin.
In the scent of a lover, the warm feeling within.

In the hop of a bunny, the smell of a flower,
The taste of fresh fruit, the sweet and the sour.

Enchantment

The list could go on, the magick is there.
I feel it right now as it blows in my hair.
I love how nature invites us to play,
And as you explore her, you'll hear her say:

"My love, my child, be curious today.
As you see me, see yourself in the same way.
Hold up a mirror, see tenderness, connection.
See the magick in you and in your reflection.

For I am you and you are me,
Your rivers, your forests and your sea.
Know you are held, all through the night.
I carry your lantern and you are the light."

Your Petals

I hear you on the breeze my love
I hear you on the breeze.
I see you being brave my love
I see you on your knees.

I invite you to the
earth my love
Come rest yourself
just here.
Curl up amongst
your petals
And know you are so
dear.

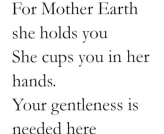

For Mother Earth
she holds you
She cups you in her
hands.
Your gentleness is
needed here
For her green and luscious lands.

Ode to the gentle people.

It's OK to Cry

Don't be afraid to cry dear one,
Don't be afraid to cry.
The feelings run so deep I know
But don't be afraid to cry.

You selflessly help all others
When they're sad, or in pain.
You wake up day after day
And you do the same again.

But this time it's so different
You feel there's nowhere to hide
You can't bury yourself in things to do
You are invited to go inside.

But here it is so grievous
So much suffering and pain.
But sit here dear one and feel,
And feel and feel again.

You owe it to yourself dear one,
so sit down by and by.
Let it all in. Let it all out.
But don't be afraid to cry.

Goddess Tree

Oh Goddess Tree, oh Goddess Tree,
Oh how I'd love to sit with thee.
Your arms reach out to east and west
Your head in the north, your feet in the south.
Your roots are grounded in the earth
And Father Sky he knows your worth.

Oh Goddess Tree, oh Goddess Tree,
Oh how I'd love to sit with thee.
You know your stillness, your place in the land.
The birds in the air come sit on your hand.
You stand in your space for all to see
At home with your vulnerability.

Oh Goddess Tree, Oh Goddess Tree,
Now I see I can sit with thee.
I don't need to travel, there's nowhere to go
The place you reside I already know.
For you reside inside of me
My beautiful, vulnerable Goddess Tree.

Poems

The Land of Morlie Grace

There's a nimpty in my heart space
It's hurting really bad.
There's a knot here in my belly
Its pressing on my flad.
And the ache here in my body
It calls me to a place.
A place that's deep inside of me,
The land of Morlie Grace.

And I breathe...

As I sit here in that garden
In the land of Morlie Grace.
The wind is blowing in the trees
The sun shines on my face.
The earth she is so happy
There are jumpties everywhere.
And everything you touch and see
Is free without a care.

And I breathe...

The trees they sing a song of love
And connecting to us all.
The flowers understand this talk
And relay it to the Frawl.
The Frawl they pass that language on
To the spiders and the ants
And all the creatures everywhere,
Right down to the frangipants.

And I breathe...

The last to hear are the humans
This universal message of love.
But sure enough the eagle flies
And sprinkles them from above.
The humans walk with heavy feet
And a stone that's in their belly
Unsure of the land of Morlie Grace
They've not seen it on the telly.

And I breathe...

But the humans' ears grow bigger
And their hearts begin to swell
Their Frungle starts to fill with love
As they close their eyes and smell.
And then they start to notice
The land of Morlie Grace.
Where no one cares for haircuts
Or what's upon their face.

And I breathe...

Where hearts are free and open
And connected to the earth.
And all of life is precious
And all beings have their worth.
And as they journey often
To this new place they have found,
They realise that they are nature
And nature is all around.

And I breathe...

Blue Bill

Today I have Blue Bill with me
He's a little, sad, blue blob.
He sits here in my tummy
and I feel I need to sob.
He sits here in my throat
encouraging out some sound.
Reminds me simply that he's here
It's real when he's around.
You see, he brings such life with him
Such clarity and truth.
I welcome him in with a big warm hug
In my home, he is my roof.

Sadness

Today there was a sadness
as I opened up the door
I asked the sadness to come in
but she sat there on the floor.

She didn't want to talk to me
She didn't want to play
So I sat there on the earth with her
and hugged her anyway.

Flibberty Floo

What should I do with this flibberty floo,
 it seems to have gone all crunky?
Where should I go with the summerdy doe, and
why must it be so clunky?
How should I hold it and where does it fit, why
does it so kerflunk me?
I'll put it in there, I'll give it a squib and wait for the
flow to Crump me.

Circles

Circle in
Circle out
Circle within
Circle without
Circle on top
Circle below
Follow the circles wherever you go.

My Cauldron

Today I stir my cauldron well,
What floats to the top I n'er can tell.
But whatever does I'll breathe it in,
Expand my chest and deep within,
My big green heart will hold it there
Synthesize it into love and air.
And then I'll breathe it out to you
To fill your big green heart up too.

Oak

The mighty oak stands strong and tall,
If you listen you will hear him call.
He'll talk to you of truth and love
Of feeling your roots and rising above.
He'll tell you stories of what he's seen,
Of who's walked past and who they've been,
And if you stop and listen too,
Who knows... one day, he'll talk of you.

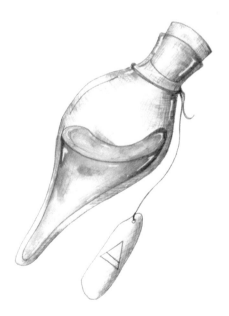

Please don't ignore our trees!

Feet

Have you ever looked down at your feet
As you were walking down the street?
What do you think your feet would say
If you were to ask them, "How's your day?"
If you were to say, "Gee, thank you feet
For carrying me, you are so neat."

I've been walking now 47 years,
They have not moaned
There's been no tears.
"I thank you feet for being you
For holding me and staying true

For hopping and skipping and dancing around
For splashing in puddles
The adventures we've found

I promise to notice you everyday
If you need anything, you just need to say."

Poems

Barefoot Silent Walk

My little barefoot silent walk in the woods
tonight was so rich. Usually I walk through
the meadow where the ground is soft.
Tonight I was called to walk through the
forest. It seems no matter how mindfully
you walk this path there will always be mud,
hard rocks, brambles scratching you and
prickles underfoot. But these things remind
you that the beauty of soft grass, smooth
tree roots and rich earth that is also on the
path.

Acceptance and love of it all is delightful.

Thank you Mumma for all of your
teachings, they always come at the
right time.

Gratitude.

Tree Wisdom

I sit in the wisdom of my old oak tree
I talk to her and she talks to me
We talk of joy and we talk of pain
We reach for the sun
and we dance in the rain.

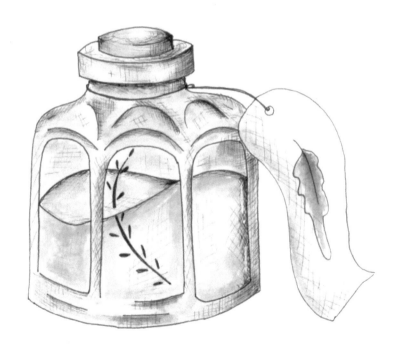

Doors

Have you ever stopped to notice?
There are so many doors
Everywhere you go
There are so many doors.
There are
Large doors
Old doors
Doors that are locked
Doors that are open
Doors that are blocked.
Big doors
Thin doors
Doors that are new, doors that are old
And doors that are blue.
Short doors
Skinny doors.
Doors that are wide
Doors with magical kingdoms inside
Trap doors
Revolving doors
Doors that look nice
Doors to avoid
Doors to entice.

All that I know
If it's doors that you seek
Any door that's open
Please take a peek.

Nymph

There's a Nymph who lives inside of me
She loves to come and play
I didn't used to hear her call,
But now she's here to stay.
She's a young and beautiful maiden
A protector of the trees
A Dryad of the forest
A friend to all she sees.
We go on great adventures
Deep in the woods to explore,
She weaves fronds of fern in my hair
As we walk the forest floor.
We sit and talk to fairies
We see people rushing by.
They always have a place to be
We sit and wonder why.
With a crown of jewels upon my head
In the moss we nap,
She leans against our Oak tree
And I lay there in her lap.
We listen to the breeze
We watch the squirrels play
At home there's just the two of us

Oh, what a beautiful day.
I visit the forest regularly
If I don't, then she will fade
She will be lost forever
And this connection we have made
So, if you hear a calling
To sit down with a tree,
Maybe Tree Nymph beckons you
And invites you to be free.

Deep in the woods

Deep in the woods where nobody goes,
Lives a beautiful dragon.
She is the colour of the trees
and if anyone were to pass her,
she would stand so still
that most humans (who often times don't
notice an awful lot anyway) would pass her by.

Her scales feel like the softest of silks
and when you run your hand across her muzzle,
you are filled with the most wondrous, magical,
mystical, powerful energy and strength.

Her eyes are the size of your head,
the colour of the softest, warmest hazel,
with an orange flash across their centre.
When you gaze into them,
you can see your own reflection smiling back at you
adoringly.
You can lose yourself here gazing through these
windows.

Her name is Feno and she is the goddess of fire.
When I am with her I sense her fire within me.
And as we lie here together gazing up at the trees,
I feel a deep peace, a knowing.
As I lay in the earth of yesterday's tears,
I feel strong and alive.
For today I rest in she.

RITUALS / CEREMONIES

These Rituals and Ceremonies have been included in this book of Enchanted writings to invite you to explore the magic in you.

By inviting these into my life it has rekindled me with childlike wonder and the joy to play.

Fairy Healing Circle

The month of June, is a time for joy... but not for all. If you are feeling the heavy energy right now, or feeling unwell, create your own fairy healing circle.

How to Create a Fairy Healing Circle

Find an area outside or near a window. You can visualise the following if you want to lay down.

Put on some music that uplifts you. If you are visualising this, light a candle. Lay down, listen to the sounds of nature.

Prepare your Altar

While the music plays, make a circle on the earth. Use candles, flowers, petals, biodegradable glitter, ribbons. Make an offering for the Fae.

When you are done, switch off the music and step into your circle. Chant the following as you dance in your circle, (throwing herbs, glitter, blowing bubbles as you go):

Fairy children come and play.
Brightest blessings to the Fae.
Come and join me on this night.
Let's celebrate our earthly rite.

Chant this and dance as long as you choose, feel the energy of the Fae around you. Feel the breeze on your face, the smell of the summer, sense everything around you.

When you are done, lay down in your circle.
Feel the gifts of the Fae.

Let them fill you with love, joy, peace, and happiness.

Lay here and breathe as long as you need, drop deep into your breath.

When you are full, open your eyes.

Thank the Fae before you leave your circle.

Give Gratitude.

Gaze Meditation

Every day, for as little as five minutes, sit with something from nature. You can choose a flower, a plant, a tree or a blade of grass. Just sit with it, sit in silence.

Tune into your breath and imagine you are breathing together.
Feel that connection.
Gaze at your flower or whatever you have chosen.

See how the light reflects on it. Gaze.
Look at its colours. Gaze.
Really focus in, like a zoom lens on a camera.

Look at its lines, curves, veins. Gaze.
Look at its contours. Gaze. Breathe together.
Notice any emotions or feelings that arise as you do this. Welcome them.

Let this feeling deepen your relationship with this plant or flower. Gaze. Breathe.
Let that relationship feed you.
Allow your body to be filled with gratitude.

Send this gratitude out into the world. We are all lines and contours, we are all colours and shadow, we are all curves and veins, we are all love, we are all beauty, we are all connected.

Earth, Air, Fire, Water.

Sound Meditation
(Similar to Gaze Meditation)

This morning I have been blessed with two visitors, Mr and Mrs Robin, building a nest in my garden. I sit and watch them come and go. I take some time to listen.

Find a place to sit outside, if you can't, open a window and sit near it.

Close your eyes,
Tune into your breath.
Relax your body. Let it sink heavy into the chair.

Listen to the birds singing.

Visualise them busy about their day, nest building.
As you breathe, listen to their song.
Tune in to one particular song, like tuning into the radio, turning the dial.
Focus in on that one song.

Imagine your breath is inhaling it deep within you.
Follow the song.

Follow it intently. Breathe.
Notice any feelings or emotions.
Allow them to flow through you as you breathe in your song, their song.

Hum your own song if it calls you.
Feel that connection.

Let it fill you with song, with joy, with love and gratitude.

Little Robin

Little Robin in the tree
Thank you for coming and sitting with me.
You bring me peace, you make me smile
And in this space I sit a while.

How happily you sing and play
Busying yourself for a whole new day.
Gathering twigs high up above
Building your nest, filling it with love.

You remind me of our gift of song
I solemnly swear that from now on,
I'll sing my heart out to all I greet
Merry part and merry meet.

Scan the QR code for a guided meditation

How to Make Life Sacred

Sacred means something or someone that is worthy of awe and respect. You are worthy of awe and respect. Your daily doings are worthy of awe and respect. If you make every act, every moment, minute, hour, day, sacred, your cup will be filled, nay, overflowing with love and adoration for yourself, others and Mumma Earth.

When all of life becomes sacred, your breath will whisper to the breeze. Your tears will flow to the ocean. The joy in your heart will warm even the sun. You will feel the stillness between it all. The stars will twinkle through your eyes and Mumma Earth's green and lush lands will grow as you grow alongside her.

Find a moment every day to commit to making something sacred, whether it's a task or a household chore. Set aside a particular time slot. Just 5 seconds, 5 minutes or 5 hours, commit.

Build on this time every day. Here's an example:

Hanging up washing!
I become aware of my feet on Mumma Earth
I become aware of my posture
I become aware of my breath
I allow my breath to flow like the ocean
I relax my body (unclench that jaw, drop your shoulders)
I become aware of the sounds around me.
As I glance at the washing, what colours do I see?
All beautiful pure whites, or a vast rainbow of colour?

As I pick up the first item, what do I feel with my sacred hands?
Is it rough, smooth, fluffy? Warm, cold?
What does it smell like?
As you hang it on the line what does the peg feel like?

Hang up the item and watch it blow on a breeze, before you reach for the next item. Breathe intentionally all of the while. See if you can do this for the whole basket.

At the end. Give Gratitude.

Succinctly... tips

Breathe. Relax. Tune into your senses (see, hear, smell, taste, feel).

When you are finished you can speak out loud if you choose:

So much gratitude for the gift of sight
So much gratitude for the gift of smell
So much gratitude for the gift of taste
So much gratitude for the gift of touch
So much gratitude for this gift of life.
Go play, have fun, be curious, enjoy, be love.

Build Yourself A Simple Altar

My altar is made up of simple things from nature and a candle.

An altar is "a flat-topped table to focus ritual ceremony and prayer" (OED)

For me it is a place I can come to, to show up. To sit and breathe, sing, listen to music or the birds, move, drum, dance, meditate, write and give thanks for being alive.

1. Find a space in your house, a corner if possible or somewhere near a window (not essential.) Find a space that will be away from the TV/internet/ busy part of the house. Make this your patch, no matter how small.

2. Find a table or cloth or both. Set them in your space. If you are not able to leave what you create permanently, use a cloth so you can gently pick it all up and put it in a drawer ready to pick up for next time.

3. Find a candle and some things that are personal to you, or have meaning. No photos or things that remind you of other people. This space is JUST for YOU.

Suggested items: a stone you found on the beach or on a walk; an ornament that's important to you; some things from nature. Perhaps things you have foraged or a bunch of flowers or a plant. As many candles or fairy lights as you choose. Some incense or sage to burn or an oil burner. A notebook and pen for anything you wish to write. A speaker if you want music. Any musical instruments you use.

4. If you like (optional) you can think of the four elements when you collect your things. Earth: stick or stone/cone. Air: a feather/incense. Fire: candle/sage/anything orange or red. Water: a shell/anything blue. This really doesn't matter. It's a reminder that you are made up of the elements, as is your altar. You choose.

5. When you have a collection of all your things, cleanse the space with sage incense or essential oil (spray or burner). Set all your things out where

you want them. As you do so, play a song of your choice, or sing a song or mantra to make your space sacred. Maybe "this space is for me and me alone, all are welcome here, here I can rest."

6. Now your altar is set, light your candle and sit in front of your space on a cushion or a chair. Sit and watch the flame of your candle as it casts a gentle warm light over your sacred space. Remind yourself that the light from the candle represents your very own light that you carry with you, your life force, your inner spark.

7. Introduce yourself to your space. Talk to it and tell it you will return as often as you can. You can sing or write or just sit and watch the candle. Whatever emotions arise in your space, all are welcome; tears, laughter, anger, pain. All are welcome.

This space will always be here. You can add to it as you choose. Come sit in this space as often as you can. To breathe, rest, write, sing, cry, do whatever you need.

Know you are loved.

Bath Time Meditation from a Mermaid

Prepare your bath.
Light candles and add some essential oil to the running water.

As you drop your robes to step in, say to yourself "I will let go."

Lay and float as long as you need.
Watch your thoughts.
Let them swirl around your mind and into your bath water.
You are one with the water, all of you.

Now lay on your back and drop your ears under the water.
Close your eyes.

Straight away you can hear your heart beat, your life force.

Now listen to your breath, it sounds just like ocean waves.

You are floating in the ocean, letting go.
If you like, you can hug your knees in to your chest and stay here.

At this point picture yourself under the ocean, swimming and exploring; use your imagination! (I became a mermaid and met some mer people who gave me a blue sapphire).

If you don't want to do this, just float.

When you are ready, sit up slowly and stand.
Watch the water run down your body and into the bath tub.

You've let it all go, keep saying "I let it all go."

Step out of the tub, like a queen or king, smile.
Step back into your robe.

Pull the plug.

Stand and watch all the water go down the plug hole.

Say to yourself, "I let go of all that no longer serves me and I offer it to Mother Earth."

Gratitude and love.

Water

It's been such a wet winter. It can begin to make you feel stuck and heavy. Imagine being a soaking-wet shirt, heavy on a washing line, imagine big, thick, muddy puddles that suck your feet down and make your bones damp and cold.

From this place of 'mind', there we will stay, stuck. Every interaction we have with others and ourselves, will be from this place, heavy, stuck, irritated, impatient for spring but...

What if we remind ourselves, that water element promotes movement: the rivers flowing, the drops of rain moving down our window pane, the beautiful reflections and patterns it makes.

Maybe Mumma Earth is inviting us into our hearts, inviting us all to flow, to feel our own internal waters, our rivers and streams.

From this place there is only beauty, gratitude and love. Every interaction we have with others and ourselves, will come from here, a place of loving, flowing, acceptance of ever-moving, ever-changing life.

There is so much gratitude for the water element, moving within you today. Drop your shoulders, relax your jaw, flow, smile or cry. Feel the beauty.

Fill Your Teapot Meditation

Find yourself a teapot or cup.
Sit somewhere comfortable.

Hold the empty teapot/cup in front of
your heart or in front of your belly.

Sit and close your eyes.
Tune into your breath.
Say out loud what you will fill your cup with,
for example:
"Today I will fill my cup with
love/peace/joy."

As you say this, imagine you are breathing it
in with the in breath and filling up your tea
pot/cup with the out breath.

Visualise all the things that make you feel this as you
do so. For example if you chose Love, you may
imagine flowers, a loved one, a child,
a summer's day.

Let your mind flit from one image to the next as you
breathe it all into your cup.
Do this for as long as you chose.

When you are ready, open your eyes.
Pour yourself a cup, drink, let it fill you up.
As you drink, say to yourself, "I fill myself
up with…"
Give Gratitude.

Scan the QR code for a guided meditation

STORIES

Every child learns to understand their world through stories. Hearing the words sparks their imagination and transports them to a magical world of make-believe.

As adults, you can reconnect to that child within when you open your heart and allow the words of the stories in this section to enchant you into a world where your spirit is free.

The Dragon Who was Different

A long time ago in a magical forest, which is of course my favourite place, there lived a beautiful baby dragon. He was covered in stunning shades of green scales. Some of them changed colour when the sun shone. He looked like a little pearl. He had pearlescent scales, he was a beautiful dragon to see.

He loved to play with his brothers and sisters in the forest; they would have so much fun. All the woodland creatures knew how beautiful and gentle he was, so he would even play with smaller creatures, like rabbits, mice and even the ants. He became popular. He was so fun-loving and full of confidence. One sunny morning he felt a little warm and he said to himself, "I need a drink, I'm thirsty." So he walked down to the lake. As he was quenching his thirst, gulping the delicious water deeply, he caught sight of his reflection for the very first time.

He noticed on his cheek there was a scale missing. Just one scale. There was a small mark where there was skin, but no scale.

"Eeewwww, look at me!" he said. "I thought I was a beautiful, majestic dragon of the forest. Look at me! I'm hideous. I'm not as perfect as I thought. What am I to do?"

He felt so lost. He decided that the best thing he could do was to go and hide in a cave. He didn't want everyone to see him. What would they think, if they saw he had a scale missing from his face? If they saw that he wasn't perfect after all!

No one would like him anymore; he'd be much better off just being on his own.

Poor dragon, he took himself off and he found a cave. There he stayed, feeling sorrier and sorrier for himself, it was such a shame. He had thought he was so perfect.

Time passed by and he grew into a beautiful, majestic dragon. But he couldn't see that, because, he just felt so imperfect. He still had that mark on his cheek that everyone would see.

One morning, when he was sitting in his cave, not used to seeing any passers-by, a young deer skipped past.

"Good morning Dragon," she said. The dragon didn't answer. He pretended not to be noticed. But the deer approached him, "How are you? We haven't seen you for a long time."

Well, the dragon didn't know what to say; he felt so embarrassed and ashamed, he didn't even want to make eye contact. He also didn't want to be rude, but, what should he say? "I'm fine here in my cave," he mumbled.

"You seem very sad," the deer said, tenderly.

The poor dragon began to cry. He told the deer the story of how he went down to the water and noticed the mark on his cheek; he told her about the missing scale on his cheek. He told her how he felt so much shame because he thought he was perfect.

"I know how that feels," said the deer. "Look, I have a crooked ear. See how my ear bends at the top." She had a sudden thought.

"You are right Dragon, maybe I should live here in the cave with you. Because I thought I was beautiful too. Look at these lovely spots on my back. Most deer lose them, but I kept mine. And what about my ear? You are right, you are right Dragon. We are not perfect, yet all the other creatures are! I've looked at all the other deer, they are amazing. They have the most perfect ears that stand upright and they twitch whenever they hear sound. My ear doesn't do that properly because it's all bent. Oh dear."

She hesitated. " Can I come and live with you?"

So she did. She stayed in the cave with the dragon. And they lived there together, pleased to have some company, but still both very sad that they just weren't perfect.

One morning, a little skunk walked past, scurrying around in the leaves.

"Good morning Dragon. Good morning Deer," he said cheerily.

"How are you both?"

The deer looked at the dragon and said, "We are living in this cave now, you might want to go somewhere else."

"Why would I do that?" Skunk replied.

"Because we are not perfect, Dragon has a missing scale on his cheek and I have a broken ear," the deer said, mournfully.

"Oh… well, I have a claw missing, does that mean I'm not perfect either?" Skunk gasped.

"Yes it does, " the deer and dragon replied together.

"Oh, well, should I come and live with you then? I have noticed that all the other skunks have such beautiful claws. I've seen them, they are so shiny. They are so long and sharp. But mine, oh no; this one is all crooked and twisted and this one is missing and mine don't shine at all. You are absolutely right. I'm not perfect either."

So Skunk moved in with Dragon and Deer. Now the three of them lived there. And that same story continued for some time. Until before you knew it, living in the cave with Dragon, Deer and Skunk, were a selection of mice, a few bunny rabbits, some birds, and a blue tit with a sore throat. There were some little caterpillars, a fox, a shrew. There were so many different woodland creatures, living in this cave together.

In their village of imperfect animals and creatures, the woodland started to go very quiet. It was very quiet indeed. The first animal to notice this was Wise Old Owl.

He thought to himself one evening, "Where are all the bats? I normally see them at night. There are not as many mice either? Also, no woodland creatures have been coming to me for advice… how curious. What is happening here?"

So that night he decided to stay up, into the daytime. When normally he would sleep, he decided to stay awake. And sure enough, there weren't as many birds in the sky, in fact there were hardly any. It was very quiet. Worryingly quiet. He couldn't see any deer hiding in the hedgerow; he didn't see any rabbits hopping about. Nor did he see any butterflies, or buzzy bees. Where had everyone gone?

He sat there all day contemplating. And as he sat there in the silence, he could hear a noise from far off. As we know, owls have magnificent hearing. He decided to go and explore. And sure enough, on the other side of the woodland, he discovered a cave. And it was swarming with life. It was full to the brim, with all the woodland creatures.

There was Dragon with his missing scale, Deer with her broken ear. And Skunk with his missing claw.

Not forgetting Bunny Rabbit who only had one
tooth, Blue Tit with the sore throat, and Caterpillar
who was the wrong colour. Of course, you could
also find Fox who didn't have a white tip on his tail
like his family, and Bat who couldn't see too well in
the daytime. Ohhhh… the list went on and on.

After Wise Old Owl sat and listened to all their
stories he said to them, "Do you realise, the whole
of the woodland is empty. You are ALL here. All of
you are imperfect," he continued, "Let me tell you a
secret."

He lifted his beautiful brown wings, high up into the
air, such beauty and grace to behold. And just at the
base of his right wing, there it was…
A bald patch!

"Ooooooohhh!" all the woodland creatures gasped
in surprise.

"Even the wisest of all of us isn't perfect either. How
silly we have been! We didn't realise, we didn't know
we were all here. We are all imperfect. Not one of us
is perfect in anyway. WE are all perfectly imperfect.

And that's the way we are made to be."

How happy they all were. So happy, they began to laugh and laugh and laugh at how silly they had been thinking such a silly thing.

The Gout Weed and the Caterpillar

One beautiful sunny day, some tiny little caterpillars were born and they all wriggled off across the meadow, to munch and munch and munch. One little caterpillar, went to wriggle across the meadow and it started raining. He sought refuge under a beautiful gout weed. If you haven't seen a gout weed before, they are long stalked plants with umbrellas on top, made up of tiny white flowers.

Caterpillar snuggled and sheltered under this gout weed for a time. He soon realised just how warm and cosy it was. He had all the food he needed to eat. And he was safe and sheltered here. He didn't need to go anywhere. So he said to himself, "I think I will stay here. I think I will stay here where I'm safe and sheltered. This is my place. I don't need to go off over there into the meadow with my brothers and sisters. I'm going to stay here."

Just then, a voice spoke and it was the gout weed. She asked, "Little Caterpillar, why aren't you going with your brothers and sisters?"

"I just feel really safe here," the caterpillar answered.

"Ok" replied the gout weed. "You can rest here a time and I'll keep you safe."

Every day, the weather would change and Caterpillar would sit beneath the gout weed. They would have beautiful conversations and he would feel so safe and held. He would gaze out and look at the sun and say "Look at that sun, if I went out there, it would surely burn my skin and I would melt."

And when it rained he would say, "Look at that rain, if I went out there when it rained, I would get washed away, or I would drown."

When it was windy he would say, "Look at that wind, if I went out there I would surely get blown away and no one would be able to save me. Here I feel safe and here I will stay."

The gout weed and the caterpillar had a wonderful friendship; she was such a nurturing gout weed. A very special gout weed indeed. The caterpillar loved her so much.

One day the gout weed said to the caterpillar, "Caterpillar, I need to talk to you."

"Sure," he said, "let's talk."

"This time I need to talk to you about something very important," she said. "All things come to an end little Caterpillar," she explained. "All things follow cycles and my life is coming to an end. My one wish before I reach the end of my cycle and I offer my body to Mother Earth, is that I see you crawl to the other side of the meadow."

"Oh!" said Caterpillar, nervously.

He continued. "I don't know, the sun is a bit hot and the wind is just too windy for my delicate skin. The rain, well it will make me so wet and oh, I would just wash away. I can't do it Gout Weed. I do love you but I just can't do it! I just can't do it, I'm just not ready, I'm not ready yet."

"It's OK," the gout weed said lovingly. "It's OK."

And so he stayed and slowly, day by day, the gout weed began to wilt. Her flowers began to fall off and she started to turn brown. The little caterpillar noticed this change. He noticed her voice becoming quite faint. He felt very afraid, but he also remembered her one wish. He knew he didn't have long.

The next day, he woke up and he said, "Gout Weed, I'm going to do it. Here I go, I'm going out into the meadow, and I'm going to do it!"

"Oh, that's wonderful!" she said in a tired, croaky voice "I know you can do it Caterpillar, I know you can do it!"

So, he peeped his little head out and the sun hit him straight away.

"Oh!" he squealed, "it's so warm and bright and very hot, but I'm just going to keep going, a tiny bit more. Ooohhh… it's burning my skin… Ooohhh… Ooohhh… Actually… it's quite nice on my skin," and he kept wriggling further into the meadow.

"I can do this," he said. "I am strong enough." And sure enough, the sun began to warm him and his body felt more flexxxxiiiibbblllleeeemooooovable.

"Oh, this feels quite freeing," he said as he wriggled along across the meadow. "How lovely."

And then the clouds came over. It became windy. And sure enough Caterpillar noticed, "Oh…the wind…oh dear it's the wind," he said, fearfully. "Am I ready for this? Am I ready?"

The winds blew and the caterpillar braced himself and the wind… cooled his skin. It didn't blow him away for he had suckers for feet. He could crawl, with his little stubbly legs. It didn't blow him away at all. He felt even freer.

"Oh, the wind has cooled me down beautifully," he said.

So he carried on walking. Next the clouds turned grey and some rain began to fall. Drip. Drop. Drip. Drop.

Caterpillar said fearfully, "Oh, rain. It's rain, the water is going to wash me away."

And it rained, it rained and rained. It was so heavy that all the ground became really slippery. Suddenly, Caterpillar realised that his little stubbly legs were actually sliding. It was so easy for him to walk and glide and slide.

"Whhhheeeeee!" he screeched. "Whhheeee! Sliding is so much fun, I didn't realise how amazing this meadow was to explore."

Finally, he reached the other side of the meadow and he turned to look back at gout weed. She gave him a knowing smile and a nod, before her body wilted, dropped and fell to the Earth. He felt so joyous and proud of himself for his journey, but so sad that she had gone. Caterpillar curled up. He curled into a little tiny ball, and pulled some leaves over his body; there he slept, for a time.

Until one day, the sun came out and it shone on his face. Caterpillar peeped his head out and he let go of his leaves and he stretched his arms out, yawning.

"Woooooohooo!" he exclaimed. "I have wings… I have wings. Look at my colours. Look how amazing and beautiful I am!"

A gust of wind lifted Caterpillar off the meadow floor, lifting him up, up, up, into the sky. He floated on the breeze, gazing down at the meadow from a completely different perspective. He could see all the beauty around him. He felt madly in love, with this precious life of his. He realised it was so precious. Why had he not seen it before? Simply because he wasn't ready, that's all.

So, he would float above and look down at the other creatures, and they would point up in awe and say, "Look at that Beautiful Butterfly!"

And sure enough, the caterpillar knew the end of his cycle would come too. We are all born and we all die. But in the middle, there is life and there is beauty and all we have to do is fly.

The Witch Who Buried Her Hat

A long time ago, on the summer solstice eve, a beautiful baby witch was born. She was born in a cabin, in the woods, to her beautiful mother, who was also a witch. And there they lived happily. The beautiful baby grew and grew, until she was seven years old. Her mother became ill and she left this realm and went to another, leaving the little witch behind.

The witch needed someone to care for her; she was a child still, after all. Along came her Grandfather. Now, her Grandfather was not a nice man, not a very nice man at all. He told her, "You need to leave this cabin and come and live with me in the town."

Now the witch knew that there were not many trees in the town. There was hardly any nature, but she had to go. She was just small and she needed someone to look after her. So off she went.

Enchantment

When she arrived at this strange concrete place, she didn't feel at home at all. No, not at all. But there she was, and there she lived.

Before long, it was time to go to school, and the little witch decided to wear her favourite clothes. She wore her green hat, her long green skirt and her crystal necklace. But the other children laughed at her.

"You are so weird!" they would taunt.

"You are such a creep."

She learnt to ignore them.

When lunchtime came, having no friends, she would sit with the tree in the playground. She loved to talk with that tree. As you know, witches can talk to trees. But the children would giggle and say, "Ha ha, look at her, she's so embarrassing. We don't want to be friends with her, she's way too weird."

The little witch would hear all this, she would listen and it made her feel sad. So she decided to talk to her Grandfather.

That day when she arrived home from school she spoke to her Grandfather, "All the children are being mean to me," she said, sadly.

Her Grandfather replied, "It's because you are so different, so weird, you just need to blend in like everyone else, otherwise you are going to get picked on all the time. No one will like you and you will be all alone and so unsafe."

That night, the little witch conjured up a plan. She climbed out of her bed and walked back to the woodland. She sat on the Earth and all the night animals gathered around her.

The foxes, the bats and the owl, they all sat with her and they asked, "What are you doing?"

"I've come to bury my hat and my clothes," she replied. "I have to be normal, like everybody else. I have to be normal, or I'm going to be so sad, so hopeless. I'll have no friends and nobody will like me. This is what I need to do."

"Are you really sure?" the wise Owl asked. "Are you really certain?"

"YES!" she replied. "I have to do this."

So she did. She dug a hole with her hands. She dug a hole deep, deep down into the earth and she buried her hat and her clothes. She covered them over with lots of soil and she walked back home to the city. She climbed into bed. She felt very sad indeed.

She went to school the next day, and some other children spoke to her. The little witch was able to make a few friends. Her Grandfather became a little more accepting of her, although, he still wasn't a very nice man.

She lived her life like a normal person. But every night when she went to bed, she could hear the hat calling her.

"Please come and get me," it would sigh. "Please come and get me."

The little witch would ignore the voice, she would pretend she could not hear it. And sure enough night after night, the voice got quieter and quieter, until it disappeared.

The witch, she grew and she wore normal clothes and a normal hat, she had normal hair and a normal face. She even got a normal job, with normal people. Her life was normal with normal children. Everything was normal, and perfect and amazing. She had forgotten; deeply, deeply forgotten all about her hat.

Until, one day, she dropped her children off at school and she muttered to herself, "I'm going to go for a walk in the woods. I haven't been there for such a long time, I do not remember."

Off she went, and as she walked through the woods, she felt amazing. The feeling of being in the woods and the trees filled her with that tingling sensation. She loved it!

"I need to come here more often," she thought to herself. "There's something about this place; it's so magical."

The witch walked and she walked and she walked some more, until she was deep within the woods. She came upon a Hawthorn tree, and as she looked at the tree, she thought to herself, "What's that in this beautiful tree? It's, it's a little Fairy!" she squealed out loud.

"I must be going mad, I can't be seeing fairies!"

She looked again and sure enough she could see fairies, swinging in the boughs, happily singing a song. She stood and listened in awe.

"This is your tree
This is your tree
Come and see
This is your tree!"

They sang these words over and over, joyously.

"This isn't my tree," she protested. "I do love this Hawthorn tree and the smell is amazing, but it's not my tree."

Over and over they sang the song, again and again. She had no idea what they were trying to tell her. The witch stood there, with the Hawthorn tree and said to herself, "There's something really familiar about this place. I have a feeling, deep, deep in my belly. It is a strange feeling; I don't remember this feeling before."

In the blink of an eye, this tingling feeling rushed through her veins, and she remembered. Like a bolt of lightning hitting her. She remembered.

"ARGHHHHHHH!" she shrieked.

"I have a hat!
 I have a hat!
Where's my hat?
I have a hat!"

She was dancing around frantically.

"Where's my hat?"

She was crazy for this hat. She knew. She remembered.

"Where's my hat?" she shouted.

Then she heard the fairies sing, "This is your tree."

At that moment she remembered, it was underneath the tree. She fell to the earth and as soon as her hands touched the soil, a wave of emotions flowed through her. She heard a voice saying, "Hear me, hear me, don't ignore me, hear me. I'm your hat, I'm here. I'm your hat!"

It all came rushing back. She remembered all the memories that she had buried with that hat, all the magic, and all of her powers. Remembering how she could heal the earth, talk to the trees, talk to the animals, talk to the plants. How she could see things in the sky, the cloud-people, the stars, the planets. Everything was working together to communicate with her.

So she dug…
And she dug…
And she dug.

Like a crazed animal she dug deeper and deeper.

Her nails ripped, there was mud and dirt all up her arms, all over her face, in her hair; she didn't care at all. It felt amazing. And then, there it was…her hat!

As she glanced down at her hat, it felt like time stood still. It called to her softly. She reached down for it with two muddy hands and she picked it up and put it on her head and…

Ohhhhhhhh…, she felt breathless. The wind… it blew. All her magic returned to her. It filled her body with tingles. She felt so alive, so full to the brim with life. When she opened her eyes, all the colours around her had changed, everything was luminous and vibrant. The birds were louder, the earth felt richer and there were noises she had never heard before.

And she knew. She was magic and she was here. She was magic and she was a witch, here to heal the world as all witches are here to do.

And she swore this hat that she placed upon her head, would never leave her again. For this was her power, her beauty and her destiny.

The Birds Who Left the Circle

A very long time ago, at the beginning of everything, the creator, who I will call She, was sitting and looking at all of the creatures and plants that She had created. There were trees, the flowers and the grass. The birds, the badgers, the foxes, the elephants and the tigers and the dogs and the humans.

And She said to herself, "Whooo, I've been so busy, I need a rest. All of these creatures, I have placed them all in the perfect circle. They all work together perfectly. They all have this understanding that I've planted here. Life is to be lived in balance with each other. They all help and they all give and they all take in balance."

And so it was, all the creatures stood in a perfect circle, working together on the planet, in harmony.

"My work here is done," She said to herself. "I'm just going to sit back, relax and enjoy it all for a while."

And She did, for a while. Until one day, there was a beautiful swan. This swan was flying high in the sky. It was a sunny day and the swan caught sight of his wings as they flashed in the sunlight.

"Awww," he thought to himself, "I am beautiful; I am so beautiful, look at me."

He felt in absolute awe of how stunning and gorgeous he was.

Then he said to himself, "I can fly so high, and I can fly so far, I am amazing, swans are amazing, birds are amazing. In fact, now I think of it, birds are the only ones that can properly fly. Bees, fly, but not very well. Wasps… well no one likes wasps anyway. But birds… birds, they are definitely THE species. If you are going to be anything, be a bird."

Then a thought popped into his head.

"That's it, I've never realised, the trees, they are there for me. The air, the air is for the birds, just for the birds. The fruit, is for the birds, the rivers to quench our thirst, just for the birds. The trees give us shelter. This is a revelation!" he shrieked.

"I had not realised before, that everything, this entire planet, is working for the birds. We are not in the circle as I thought, we are way above it. The circle is there for us. We are here above the circle, the circle is down there," he said pointing with his wing.

"I have to tell my friends," he said, excitedly.

So off he flew to his friends. They talked and his other swan friends all agreed, and wondered why they had not realised; of course, they were above the circle, of course they were the higher species.

"We must tell everybody," they agreed. "We must tell all the birds."

So they passed this message around and around as birds are really good at singing and chattering. It wasn't long before it spread all across the world that the birds were the higher species.

With this belief, the birds would strut around like they owned the place, oh yes.

They began to get bossy. They would say, "Trees, we need more fruit. You need to feed us. We are the ones that sing and fly. You need to feed us now. Now!"

"Rivers, we need more water, we are thirsty you know. Where is our water?"

"Trees, we need more shelter, we need more leaves, grow faster!"

"Come on, hurry up!" they would demand.

They became so bossy, that all the other creatures, the plants, animals from far and wide, protested, "You know what? We've had enough of this bullying. What are we going to do?"

A meeting was called and all the animals and plants came from far and wide. There were elephants and tigers and bears and rhino. Giraffes, fleas and ants, snails and tiny mice. Even the most magnificent trees uprooted and came to this place to gather. What a sight to behold! All stood in a circle.

The first to speak was the tree, as he had the loudest voice. And he bellowed, "What are we going to do?"

"What can be done with these birds?"

"I know," said the elephant. "My gift is strength, we can squash them. I'll stamp on them with my feet, I'll whack them with my trunk. Before you know it, there will be no more birds."

"Hmmmm, I don't think that's a good idea," interrupted the rabbit.

And the idea was passed around the circle, everyone decided it wasn't a good idea.

"I know," said the ant. "We are really strong too, me and my friends can crawl all over them in swarms and we can bite them and drive them mad. They won't stay around for long."

Again ant's idea was passed around the circle. NO! NO! NO! It was not a good idea!

"Does anyone else have any ideas at all?" asked the tree.

"I know," said the tiger. "I have big sharp teeth, I can eat them all. I can kill them all, leave it with me."

"Oh no!" said the tree, "That is NOT what we want. There must be someone who has a good idea?"

Some time passed and they stood in the circle in silence.

"I have an idea," said the human. "My gift is my brain, and my brain, when used as my companion and not my master, can give me ideas. I have this thing called imagination which helps me to create good ideas. These ideas, I get from feelings. I think we need a feeling for this."

Well, the other animals didn't really know much about feelings.

"Feelings, what are these feelings?" they all enquired.

The human thought for a time and then spoke, "Ok, I want you all to close your eyes. I want you to feel the feeling of love."

They all closed their eyes but they didn't know what this feeling was, this feeling of love. They all seemed confused as they stood there with their eyes closed.

"Now," said the human, "Visualise the planet, a beautiful big green and blue ball. We are all standing on this planet, together in a circle, in harmony."

And they did, they all started to imagine.

"In the centre," the human continued, "in the very centre of this planet, is a ball of fire, with the most beautiful enchanting colours of red, orange, yellow and blue. It is whirling, whirling and churning, such beautiful embers. It is hypnotic. It sits in the centre of the earth, pure essence, and pure love. It is calling you; can you feel its warmth?"

They all nodded and smiled.

"And from this ball," the human continued, "from this ball in the centre of the earth, are tiny little channels that run up to the surface of the earth, where we are standing. It is running through the people, the animals and the plants, it runs through all living things. And each living thing in their centre has this golden ball inside of them too. It's just their smaller version of it, but all the essence and the love is still there."

The human's eyes gently opened, peeping, to make sure all were feeling this love and as they glanced around the circle, it was clear that all the animals were. They all had such happy faces.

"And," the human continued, "you can all feel this golden ball within you, this warm feeling that is love."

Do you know what? All the animals and plants in that circle stood there with their eyes closed and they felt a tingling in their bodies; they felt a warm sensation, flushing in their cheeks. They were filled with a feeling of absolute joy. They had never felt such a feeling so intensely before. How amazed they all felt!

They all opened their eyes. "This is amazing!" they all proclaimed.

"Human, you are amazing! We now know we have this feeling called love in our bodies, but what do we do with it?"

"This is my plan," said the human. "Now we can feel this, we need to share it."

"Tree," the human said. "When you go back to where you stand by the river, I want you to dip your branches in the water and fill the river with this love feeling that is coming out of your branches because now you can feel it, can't you?"

"Ooooohhhh, yes!!!" tree replied, beaming from branch to branch.

"What a great idea," said the ants. "We can scurry around in the mud and we can flick bits of love all over the ground."

"What a marvellous idea," said the mice. "We can cover the fruit with it, with our tiny little paws. We can cover the fruit with love. There will be love EVERYWHERE," they squeaked.

"Let's do it!" they all shouted in harmony.

And off they all went, back to where they lived, to spread love absolutely everywhere. When these birds would be flying in it, sleeping in it, eating it, drinking it and… anything could happen.

Sure enough, that is what they did. They sprinkled love everywhere. The birds, began to feel a bit strange.

In the swan's nest, the swan said to his partner, "I feel a bit weird today. I feel a bit umm… fluffy… Do you feel fluffy?"

"Well, yes," Mummy swan replied. "I just had a drink of that water and I think there is something in it. It tastes… well, weird. It's kind of nice though."

"Yes, I feel like that too," added Daddy swan.

Next, a bird that was flying overhead tweeted, "I just had some fruit, the fruit tastes amazing. Have you tried it? Something has happened to the fruit."

The bird too had that warm and fluffy feeling. Before you know it, there were birds everywhere and they were all tweeting to each other about this amazing feeling of love.

Then Blue Tit spoke. "I have to confess… I'm sorry, I have to confess this, but… well… I stood on the edge of a branch this morning and a breeze blew in my face. It felt so amazing that I said, thank you!" He looked puzzled.

All the other birds looked shocked. Mummy swan drew breath and said, "You said thank you! The most important species cannot say thank you. What were you thinking?"

"I know," said the little blue tit, sheepishly. "But maybe, just maybe, I thought, while I felt this breeze; maybe we are not the most important species after all? Maybe we do actually belong in the circle. In this circle, is where we would feel this thing, whatever it is."

"Oh my goodness, you are right," they all remarked. "You are right, what have we done? We need to go and see Owl."

Off they all flew to see Owl. When they arrived at wise Owl's tree, they called to him. Owl hopped out and stood on his branch, looking tired as he always did this time of the day!

"Owl!" they all stated. "We were so wrong. We want to come back in the circle. We are really sorry; we can't believe how silly we've been. How could we think that we were the most powerful above all other creatures and beings on this planet?"

"I know," said the Owl. "I knew you would figure it out eventually."

"But do you think they would welcome us back in the circle?" the birds begged.

"Of course they would," replied Owl. "Of course they would, because they love you!"

"What should we do?" the birds pleaded.

Owl ruffled his chest, sat firmly on his branch and wisely said, "In the morning, I want you to go down to where they all meet, where they all gather when the sun is rising."

The birds agreed.

The next morning just before sunrise, the birds got up and they stretched. They went down to the beautiful vast plain of land, where all the animals gathered in a circle.

At first, they stood outside the circle and tweeted to the animals, "Please, we are really sorry."

All of the animals wondered what all the fuss was about. They didn't need an apology. They instantly moved to make space for the birds. They all joined each other in harmony again, in a circle. All connected. All connected with this beautiful feeling of love.

Do you know what happened? This wondrous feeling that was in all of them became so alive, there were little shoots of golden light, sparking from one creature to the next, all connecting them. It danced

across, over, under, above, and below, left, right and centre. They realised, they weren't in a circle any more, but were in a matrix of light. It went all the way through the earth's core and through them. They were in this most magnificent globe of wondrous light. At that moment, the warm sun, a beautiful sight to behold, rose in the sky and all was connected and all was love.

"We shall call this moment, Dawn."

Mother Earth, the great creator, remarked "Ahhhhh, I knew if I gave each and everyone their beautiful gift, they could feel this love within them. They would know exactly what to do with it. These humans, they know exactly what to do, I'm so proud of all of you, Yeay!"

So, every day, if you want to feel this amazing sensation of love and being connected to all, it is there at dawn, when the sun rises. All you have to do is love and use your imagination to magic a nation for the next generation.

The Adder Who was Scared of His Shadow

One fine sunny day, on the edge of a beautiful meadow, Adder sat on his favourite rock, sunning himself. This particular day, he noticed something different. As he moved, he noticed his shadow next to him. And it made him jump.

"AAARRRGGGH!" he gasped.

"That shadow has fangs and oh, it's looking very scary. I don't think I like it out here in the sun. I'm going to go and hide under that bush. I'm a bit scared of that shadow, he just doesn't look like he normally does, I think he's a bad and evil shadow that wants to get me!"

So he hid underneath a bush in the hedgerow. He was a little bit shaken up because, the more he thought about it, the bigger the shadow felt and the bigger his fangs looked.

"I'm just not going to come out of here," Adder said. "I'm scared. My shadow scares me."

Poor Adder.

As he sat under the hedgerow, a little Rabbit hopped by. Hippity hop, Hippity hop.

"Good morning Adder," he smiled. "Are you ok?"

"Ummmm, I'm a little bit scared," Adder answered.

"What are you scared of?" asked Rabbit.

"My shadow," Adder replied. "Today I noticed my shadow, and it was really big and it grew massive fangs. It turned into a monster and tried to get me!"

"Ooooh dddeearr," Rabbit stammered. "I dddon't like the sssound of ttthatt!" and he looked around, timidly.

Adder hissed, "Sssaaaarrrrgggghhhhh… there it is again. Look, it's that shadow, standing right next to you. He's morphed into something else. Ooooh, look at his ears… no, horns… he's got horns on his head!"

And sure enough Rabbit looked down at the floor and… there it was right next to him, a massive shadow with horns on its head. Rabbit JUMPED and he ran into the hedgerows with Adder.

"You are safe here Rabbit!" Adder soothed. "There are no shadows here, you are safe."

Rabbit and Adder sat underneath the hedgerow, shaking and quivering. Sure enough, the shadow had gone.

"Phew!" they sighed.

"Ohhhh, let's do some deep breathing," Adder said, breathing IN and OUT deeply. "We are ok, we are safe, here in the hedgerow."

As they sat there, the two of them, rather shaken up, another woodland animal passed by. It was Deer, she was munching on some grass. As she was eating a little bit of the hedgerow, she saw them hiding.

"Hello," she said. "What are you doing?"

"We are hiding," Adder replied.

"Why are you hiding?" Deer asked, curiously.

"We are afraid!" said Rabbit.

"What are you afraid of?" asked Deer.

"Our shadows, they've turned into monsters!" squealed Rabbit.

"Yes," said Adder in agreement. "Mine had fangs and it was enormous, evil and dark."

"And mine!" Rabbit squealed. "Mine had enormous horns on its head and it tried to attack us!"

"Oooohhhh," Deer remarked, looking nervously over her shoulder. "That sounds a bit scary," and she looked around, feeling a bit unsafe herself.

"Aaaarrrgggghhhhh," Adder and Rabbit screeched.

"There it is again… look at it, it's grown, it's massive, it's got big long legs with claws on and an enormous head," they stammered in unison.

Sure enough, Deer looked down and she saw this evil shadow. Enormous it was, with big long legs and a humongous head.

"Arrrgghhoooooo!" Deer jumped. She ran into the hedgerow with Adder and Rabbit. And there they all stood shaking and shivering.

"Oohhh, these sh… sh shadowsss are sss….. so scary," Rabbit stuttered "What are we to do?"

"I don't know," said Adder, "But I know we are safe here, in the hedgerow, away from the shadows."

So there they stood, the three of them in the hedgerow. And as the day passed by, every so often another woodland creature would walk by and the same thing would happen. Adder, Rabbit and Deer would relay their story and another animal would join them.

Before you knew it, there was Badger, Fox and the mice and the worms and the beetles and the birds and all the woodland creatures hiding in the hedgerow, because they were afraid of their shadows.

"Uuuuhhhhhh," Adder complained. "It's getting rather cramped in here! We've got no room, what are we to do? The world has gone crazy!"

"I know," agreed Rabbit. "But let's go and see Owl, we can walk through the forest, so we don't see any shadows. We'll be safe in the forest."

"What a good idea!" Adder admitted. "Yes. Let's go."

So all of the woodland creatures went into the deep part of the forest to Owl's Tree. He lived in a beautiful, magnificent oak tree, an enormous, broad tree. They gathered around the tree and called up to Owl.

"Owl...Owl!!"

Owl appeared "Good morning," he yawned. "OH... Good morning everybody," he said surprised. "You are all here at the same time. What on earth is happening?"

"We are all very afraid!" announced Adder. "It's our shadows. All of our shadows, they've turned bad, we are so scared!" he continued.

"What happened?" asked Owl.

Adder explained, "Well, mine had big fangs and it was enormous and it was going to attack me."

Rabbit remarked, "And mine had enormous horns and big feet and it tried to jump on me."

And Deer added, "Mine had enormous legs and it tried to stamp all over me."

And the story continued. Owl patiently sat and listened to each and every woodland creature tell their story.

"We all had to hide in the hedgerow," they chorused.

"Hmmmmm," said Owl, in a very wise way.

He thought for a time, "How are we all feeling right now?"

"Very scared," remarked Rabbit.

"Ok," Owl said, "But now I'm here. You have all made your way safely through the forest away from the shadows and you are all stood here, with me and my tree. How are we all feeling now?"

"Well, I'm happy to be talking to you, because I know you'll have a solution, Owl!" Adder replied.

"So you feel happy?" said owl.

"Yes," Adder said.

"And I feel safe," said Rabbit.

"And I feel calm, nice and calm," said Badger.

"And I feel loved," said Deer.

"Now," said Owl. He took a big deep breath in and he said, "Can you all look where you are standing? Look down at the floor. What do you see?"

They didn't know what he meant and they looked a little confused.

"Step back a bit from my wise and magnificent Oak Tree and look down at the ground - what do you see? How do you all feel now? Are you still all feeling happy and safe and calm and loved?"

"Yes," they all replied.

"Look at the ground," Owl commanded. "Where are you all standing?"

"Ummm… in the forest?" answered Rabbit.

"Yes," said Owl. "But what's on the floor, what can you see?"

"Well I can see the shadow from… the Oak…tree…"

"Aaaaahhhh," they all gasped.

"We are standing in the magnificent Oak Tree's shadow!" they exclaimed.

"Yes!" said Owl. "You are standing in the Oak Tree's shadow and you all feel, happy, safe, calm and loved."

And they all went a little quiet.

"So, if we feel happy and safe and calm and loved, standing in the shadow of the Oak Tree, then maybe shadows aren't that scary after all?" suggested Adder.

"Hmmmm," said Rabbit. "Maybe shadows are our friends?"

And they all decided, there and then, that Owl was right. They did feel safe and happy and loved and calm in the shadows. They didn't feel scared. There was no fear after all.

And so they all ran out into the sunshine and they danced with their shadows. What a beautiful sight to behold!

The Snail Who Didn't Grow

Not so long ago, not so long ago at all, a lovely little snail, just starting his life, was crawling across the grass of the meadow very slowly, as snails do. His brothers and sisters were there too, all crawling across the meadow with him.

The snail just noticed, as they all went off in their own direction to begin their lives, that he was a bit smaller than the others. This started him thinking about being small.

So off he went, munching, munching, munching and he found himself a beautiful rock next to a river. It had a perfect little nook that he could slide his body into and a perfect little cup-shaped part of the rock that he could just lay his shell in. He loved just resting there for a time, watching the river. He would see other animals passing by and he would munch and rest and munch and rest. But also, he would worry. He would think about how small he was, and whether or not he had grown.

So every day he would wake up and look at his shell.

"I don't think I've grown again. I haven't grown," he would sigh.

He would munch and munch and rest and munch and munch and rest. And wake up and look at his shell and say "I haven't grown, I'm just not growing. I don't know what's happening; I'm just not growing at all."

He did this for quite some time until one day he woke up, so worried, he decided he must get some advice about his problem.

He thought, "I'll ask someone for advice, maybe they'll have some tips, I'm only a small snail, maybe they can help. I will ask how they grow, what they do… yes."

He waited patiently for the next passer-by. Sure enough, the first animal to pass by was Rabbit. Hippity hop, Hippity hop.

"Rabbit!" called Snail.

"Yes?" Rabbit replied, screeching to a halt.

"Can you give me some advice?"

"Of course I can!" replied Rabbit. "How can I help?"

"Well," said Snail "I'm a bit sad because I'm not growing. I'm just not growing at all."

"Hmmm," thought Rabbit "Oh dear, well ummm, do you eat?"

"Yes," Snail nodded.

"Hmmm well that's right," said Rabbit. "as that's what I do… I also do a lot of hopping, I hop and hop and hop. I'm sure that must have helped me grow," he said showing off his hopping skills.

"Well," said Snail "I don't do that, so maybe that's what I need to do. Thank you so much for your advice," he said.

"You are welcome," Rabbit replied, hopping off into the meadow.

185

So, Snail sat there and he thought, "Hmmmm, so maybe I need to learn to hop. Right here goes," he said.

"Eeeeeeeekkkk ekkkkkk ooooo!" he squealed, as he made the funniest noise trying to squish himself off the floor. But try as he might, his big body would not lift off the floor. All Snail managed to do was slide off his rock.

"Oh, I can't do it," he grumbled, "my body is too big, it sticks to the floor. I'm never going to learn how to hop. I'll have to ask someone else for advice."

Snail sat there a time, feeling a bit sad, waiting for the next passer-by.

The next animal to pass was Mouse, who was scurrying along.

"Mouse!" Snail called.

"Yes?" Mouse squeaked. "I'm very busy."

"Can I ask you for some advice? It won't take a moment."

"Ok," Mouse mumbled, looking very busy. "How can I help?"

"Well," Snail said. "I'm very sad, because, I'm just not growing. And I wondered if you could tell me how you grew?"

"Oh dear," said Mouse. "I don't know much about growing, but I grew, just a little enough."

"Well what did you do?" asked Snail, eager to hear Mouse's reply. "How did you grow?"

"Well," said mouse. "I did lots of eating, yes, lots of eating."

"Well," said Snail "I already do that!"

"Well the other thing I do is I run and scurry about all over the place. Really fast, like this," she said, showing off her running skills.

And off she scurried; she was very busy after all.

"Hmmmmm," Snail thought. "So I need run and scurry, so let's try that… ok."

He stretched his body and had a little wriggle, limbering himself up.

"Let's get ready for running and scurrying," he said. "Here I go. Eeeeeee du du du du du huuuugggggghhhhh!" were the funny noises he made, trying so hard to make his big squishy body go faster. But it just would not happen.

Snail let out a big sigh and began to cry. "It's no good!" he said to himself. "I can't run and scurry, everything I do is slow. I'm never going to grow!" he sobbed.

Snail sat on his rock, so very sad, oh so sad, poor snail. As he sat there feeling sad for himself, who walked past, but Duck.

"Quack, Quack, Quack, Good morning Snail, why are you so sad?"

"Heh, heh, heh," Snail sobbed, "I'm just not growing. And nothing I do is going to make me grow. It's just not happening."

"Oh," said Duck, "Are you eating lots of good food, vegetables, plants and healthy things?"

"Yes," Snail sighed. "I do that all of the time."

"You know the other thing I do, is walk. I do lots of walking. I do swimming too, but lots of walking, I love to walk."

"Maybe that would help?" Snail suggested, hopefully.

"Maybe," said Duck as she waddled off. "I hope you feel happy again soon Snail."

"Well," said Snail, to himself. "I don't walk the same as Duck but I can move. I move slowly, but I move. Maybe that what I need to do to grow?"

And sure enough he did, that day snail decided to leave his rock behind and walk and munch and walk and munch and that is what he did. For a long time, for many days, weeks, even months, he walked and munched. But still every day, he would glance back at his shell and worry and worry.

"I still have not grown," he would say. "This has all become too much! I need to do something!" He thought for a time.

"Ah ha, of course," he said. "I need to go and see Owl. Of course, he is the wisest in the woods. He will know what to do."

So off he went, at a very slow pace, to see Owl.

When he arrived at Owl's tree, out popped Owl's head.

"Good morning," he hooted, yawning and stretching.

"Good morning," Snail said. "I wonder if you can help me Owl."

"I'll try," Owl replied.

"I've been trying to grow, trying so hard to grow," Snail stated. "I've tried hopping, running and scurrying and finally, I've tried walking. I've been eating and eating and doing all the right things you should do to grow, but I'm not growing," he said sadly, gazing at the floor. "Every day I look back at my shell and I'm the same size, I just don't change. I don't know what to do Owl, can you help?"

"Mmmm … " pondered Owl. "Every day you look at your shell? Every day you watch your shell?"

"Yes," replied Snail. "And it doesn't grow at all!"

191

"Ok," replied Owl. "Snail, this is what you need to do. Do you remember, at the beginning of your story, you used to sleep on a rock?"

"Why, yes," replied Snail. "That was my happy place. I liked that rock."

"And you slept on that rock long before you began munching and walking and hopping and running?" quizzed Owl.

"That's right," Snail replied.

Remembering this beautiful place, he smiled and he said. "It had a perfect little cup shape for my shell, and a lovely little nook just next to the river for me to rest my body in."

"Well, I say you need to go back to that place. You need to go back to your rock, today and have a nice sleep on it," said wise Owl.

"Hmmm … " thought Snail, "that's an interesting idea!" Snail didn't understand why Owl would suggest this but seeing as Owl was the wisest in the wood, he agreed. "Ok Owl, I will do that. Thank you."

So off he went, slowly, as snails do, back to his rock. When he finally arrived he could see his rock in the distance. The space was heavenly.

"Ooohhh, my rock!" he shouted.

He couldn't wait to sit on his rock. He slithered over to his rock next to the river and he looked and found the gorgeous little nook he slept in.

As he prepared his body to slide in, and he slid his nose and his face into the nook and then his body.. his b.o.d.y...

"Huuuurrggghh," he said as he tried to squeeze in. "Huuuurrggghh." It didn't quite fit. "What's happening?" Snail said, looking confused.

"Somebody has moved my rock, or done something with my rock! Is this the same rock? Yes, it's the same rock, but it's, it's, shrunk!" he said, scratching his head.

"How strange," he thought, "maybe I'll try and rest my shell on it instead, yes, my favourite bit."

So, as he rolled slightly on his side, his shell went, "Clink... clink... clink," on the rock.

"It's not fitting! It's not fitting! I can't get in the nook and my shell is not fitting in here and... what is happening? What has someone done to my rock? I can't get in, I'm too big!" he said, confused.

He then thought for a moment.

"TOO BIG!" he laughed.

"I'm TOO BIG!" he shouted with glee.

"I'm TOOOOO BIIGGGG!" he hollered, at the top of his voice in excitement. He laughed and laughed, "Ha, ha, ha, I have grown!" he yelled.
"I have grown!"

Snail let out a sigh of relief as he realised how silly he had been. He laughed and laughed and laughed.

He decided to sit on his rock, in a different way, in a comfortable, new position and he slowly adjusted his body. Slowly, slowly as snails do.

He thought to himself as he watched the water rippling, "All of this time, I've been growing and I didn't know. I was so busy trying to make myself grow, trying to make something happen so I could get bigger, that it was happening anyway, I was already growing, Now here I am, bigger. Amazing!" And he felt so happy and so content.

Snail had a little nap there right on his rock, next to the river as the water rippled by and the birds sang.

It's often the way, I find, when we don't notice we are growing, the growth is happening anyway. Perhaps you can take some advice from Snail. Growth always happens at its own speed, we can't rush it. Go slow… like snails do.

The Grumpy Robin

Just a little way back, there lived a beautiful, tiny Robin. He was teeny, for he had just been born. He had cracked out of his shell, into this world. He had a lovely family, his parents adored him.

One day, when the Robin was around two weeks old, still very small and not ready to leave the nest, he fell out! He fell to the ground, he did. And much as his mother and father tried, they just could not get him to fly back up. They couldn't get him back into the nest and they were so busy looking after his other brothers and sisters that they had to leave him there. He had to find his own way.

Amazingly, he did. He grew and he managed to teach himself how to fly and off he flew high up into a tree all by himself.

Now you would think that would be something to be really proud of, amazing. But because the poor little Robin missed out on bundles and bundles of love, he was a sad Robin. He had become a sad Robin, and now was a grumpy Robin.

Every day he would wake up, watch the other Robins and copy them.

"Ok," he would say. "We get up, and we tweet, and we sing, and then we get our food - worms and grubs. We use these flappy things to dive down and get a worm and come back to the branch, and when the sun sets, we sleep."

Grumpy Robin learned to do the same thing over and over again. Every day he would get up and sing in a grumpy kind of way. He would sit on the branch in a grumpy way. He would fly down and get worms in a grumpy way. And he would go back to sleep in a grumpy way.

And repeat.

Every day he would do this. Every day he lived the same pattern. If robins wore watches he would have been looking at his every minute, wondering if it was nearly sunset so he could go to sleep. It became so monotonous, that eventually, his singing became sadder and he felt so tired all of the time and so angry.

He had no friends because of his sadness and grumpiness; nobody wanted to spend any time with him. It was such a shame for poor Robin, such a shame.

One morning Robin did not wake up, which was very out of the ordinary. He slept and he slept and he didn't wake up until it was just about sunset. The other birds where all finishing their singing and about to go to bed.

Robin woke up with a start and panicked.

"Oh, no, what time is it? What time is it? Are they singing yet?"

The other birds weren't singing.

"Oh, that orange thing is going down, that means I have to go to bed. What's happened, what's happened to the day?" he flustered, in a feathery way.

"I've slept all day and I haven't sung and I haven't got up and ruffled my feathers and I haven't jumped off and eaten a worm, and I haven't jumped back on again and sung again like all the other Robins…" He was talking so fast he could hardly think.

"I haven't joined in and … I haven't been part of the day, and nothing has changed? Everything looks the same? My branch is still here, my branch, nothing has changed. My tree is still here, nothing has changed. My nest, my tree, the sun is still setting, and the sun… is still going to rise," he said with glee (yes glee!).

Robin sat there for a time, thinking about the fact that nothing had changed and he said to himself, "When I get up in the morning, if I want to, I can sing. If I don't want to, I don't have to and nothing will change! Oh my goodness!" he gasped. "That means I have a choice?"

"That means that if I want to, I can sing. If I want to, I can eat. If I want to, I can fly. If I want to, I can do nothing. I can do what I like, I have a choice, I always have a choice!"

This was a revelation to dear Robin knowing that he had a choice. He was so excited about the next day that he couldn't sleep. He stayed awake all night. In the morning, as the sun rose, he thought to himself, "Do I feel like singing today? Hmm, no, not really!"

So, he sat there and he listened to the other birds sing, he felt the breeze on his face which he had never noticed before. He sat and watched the sun and thought, "Isn't that beautiful, I've never noticed that before."

Simply because he had time for himself and he knew that he had a choice, everything felt different, even though nothing had changed.

The next morning when he woke up, he sat there and he looked at the others and they started singing and he thought, "Ahhh, a new day, I only get to live about three years. It's a new day, I get a new day!"

Robin felt this little unusual feeling in his belly, like warm custard whirling around in his belly. He felt sparkles, sparkles, tingles in his wings, something moving in his body he didn't know – what was it? Excitement? Joy?

"Joy!" he smiled to himself.

"Me, feeling joy, happiness! Is this happiness?" he beamed.

Sure enough, the feeling in his belly began to move, up like a little slippery snake, to his throat. And as it hit his throat, it took his breath away. He took a deep breath in. He gasped, and looked up at the beautiful sky, which he also had not really noticed before. And when he breathed out, the most beautiful song came out. He had never heard himself sing like that before.

Never, never, ever, ever. It felt amazing, like there was space in his body. There was so much space that he stretched out his wings. And instead of just dropping down to pick up a worm, he jumped off the branch in sheer delight and he flew, and he drifted, and he glided and he twirled.

"I didn't realise how much fun it is to fly!" he shouted with glee, for all to hear.

All the other robins saw him, and they felt so happy for him. The wind joined in the celebration too.

When he returned to his branch, Robin felt so alive and elated. Robin was so happy to have finally found himself - his happy self. He looked forward to waking up the next morning.

Always keep in your mind, that sometimes you may see sad grumpy little Robins. But they all have their individual stories. Sometimes, all they need is a smile from someone. So let's all smile and share our smiles for all to see.

The Bee Who Gave Too Much

One day, not so long ago, there lived a beautiful bumble bee. She had magnificent brown and yellow fluffy stripes, and gorgeous little black pearl eyes. She loved collecting nectar and making honey. Bee especially loved sharing it with everybody else.

After a busy day of gathering nectar and making honey, every night she would go back home, back to her hive. Bee would often be so tired, that she would have no honey left for herself.

"That's okay," she would say. "I love to give to others."

She would sleep heavily on an empty stomach and wake up early again the next day, ready to collect more nectar and make more honey. She would follow that same routine every day until one morning…

…she woke up feeling very tired. Bee started to feel a bit cross, and short-tempered with the other bees. She gave out her honey but it began to taste bitter. The angrier she felt, the more bitter her honey tasted.

"Have some honey, yes have some honey, and have some honey. Here you go," she would say, angrily.

After a busy day, when she arrived home at night with no honey left for her she would say to herself, "Typical! None left for me. All I do is give to others and what do I get back? Nothing! Selfish, they all are selfish, selfish, and selfish." Bee was so angry and so tired.

Seeing Bee becoming so cross and angry, some of the other bees said, "It's okay, we don't want any honey. It tastes bitter."

"What do you mean you don't want any honey?" Bee replied in shock. "It's not bitter, take it!"

"Your honey now has a strange taste," the other bees said, "we don't like it anymore."

So now, when Bee came home at night, she would have some honey left over for her, but she didn't want to have it herself. She wanted to give it to others. That's what she was used to doing, she didn't know any other way. With these feelings of rejection, she would just throw the honey away and sleep on an empty stomach, tired, angry and lost.

However, one morning, she awoke early to collect nectar and as she stood balancing on a beautiful buttercup, she felt so tired, exhausted from giving all of the time, that she came over all funny and fell to the earth.

As her little body hit the ground with a jolt, she began to cry. Bee cried and cried. She cried so much that all her tears were watering the earth around her and yet she didn't notice. As she cried and cried, her tears began reaching down to the little seeds that were waiting there. Soon, the little seeds began to grow. One particular little seed grew, into a little green shoot, just high enough to cover Bee laying there, flat on her back. As the shoot covered her, it started to rain, just very lightly, spit spot, drops of gentle rain.

The sweet rain that had fallen over all the flowers and the plants began to drop gently on the little shoot. This water rolled softly down the tiny leaf and fell straight into Bee's mouth, gently feeding her some

Enchantment

of the precious droplets of love. As soon as these lovely drops of sweet water, laced with love, fell into her teeny open mouth, she stopped. She stopped crying, she stopped moving and she went completely still. Her pearly black eyes shone, she opened them wide. It felt like time had frozen as she lay there still, being held by the earth and nurtured by the little shoot. She gazed up at the most beautiful blue sky she had ever seen. She could feel the heartbeat of the earth beneath her. Around her, the green shoots were dancing and swaying on the breeze, just for her.

She felt her place in this land as she lay there giving thanks to the beautiful shoot that had brought her back to life. She realised what she had done - she had not given any love to herself at all.

"All of my love I put into my honey to give to others," she thought. "None did I save for myself and that's why the others stopped liking it, because it began to taste bitter with anger."

Now she felt connected and alive once more! Bee knew her place in this world and she decided that things would be different. Gently she stood up, finding her balance, softly kissing the beautiful green shoot. And she flew off back to her hive and then fell fast asleep.

The next morning, she woke up, she had a stretch just for herself, knowing that her body needed it. She started her day gathering nectar for honey and she would rest, when she needed it. And at the end of the day she would offer out some honey, but always to be sure to keep some for herself.

Bee's honey became very popular again. In fact, even more popular than it had been before. It was so popular, that she became the new Queen... of course.

About the Author

Bella Donna, The Green Witch, speaks from her soul. Having worn the mask of an imposter for many years, Bella decided to take matters into her own hands. She faced her demons and repelled the cloak of being ordinary to reveal a deeply passionate woman who found her true calling.

Bella is a Life Coach with a difference. With 30 years' experience in nursing, psychotherapy and Shamanic practices, her vision is a world where people find their path to authentic Connection, Joy and Freedom.

Bella's mission is to guide you on a unique transformational journey, connecting you to nature and your inner child; revealing the power of passion, play, and pleasure.

www.bella-donna.co.uk
Facebook @belladonnagreenwitch